DRIVING STANDARDS AGENCY
SAFE DRIVING FOR LIFE

the official
THEORY
TEST REVISION PAPERS
for Car Drivers

London: TSO

D0489842

Written and compiled by Driving Standards Agency (DSA) Publications.

Published with the permission of the Driving Standards Agency on behalf of the Controller of Her Majesty's Stationery Office.

First published 2004

ISBN 0 11 552619 6

A CIP catalogue record for this book is available from the British Library.

Other titles in the official DSA series

The Official Theory Test for Car Drivers
The Official Theory Test for Motorcyclists
The Official Theory Test for Drivers of Large Vehicles
Driving - the essential skills
The Official Guide to Learning to Drive
The Official Guide to Accompanying Learner Drivers
Motorcycle Riding – the essential skills
Official Motorcycling – CBT and practical test
Driving Buses and Coaches – the official DSA syllabus
Driving Goods Vehicles – the official DSA syllabus
The Official Guide to Tractor and Specialist Vehicle Driving Tests
The Official Theory Test CD-Rom – for car drivers
The Official Theory Test CD-Rom – for motorcyclists
The Official Guide to Hazard Perception DVD
Roadsense – the official guide to hazard perception VHS
The Official Guide to Learning to Drive DVD

Theory and practical tests
(Bookings and enquiries)

DSA **0870 0101 372**
Fax **0870 0104 372**
Minicom **0870 0106 372**
Welsh speakers **0870 0100 372**
Online **www.dsa.gov.uk**

DVTA (Northern Ireland)
Theory test **0845 600 6700**
Practical test **0870 247 2472**

Driving Standards Agency
(Headquarters)

Stanley House, 56 Talbot Street,
Nottingham NG1 5GU

Tel **0115 901 2500**
Fax **0115 901 2510**

www.dsa.gov.uk

Driver & Vehicle
Testing Agency
(Headquarters)

Balmoral Road, Belfast BT12 6QL

Tel **02890 681 831**
Fax **02890 665 520**

www.doeni.gov.uk/dvta

Driver & Vehicle
Licensing Agency
(GB Licence Enquiries)

Tel **0870 240 0009**
Fax **01792 783071**
Minicom **01792 782787**

www.dvla.gov.uk

Driver & Vehicle Licensing
Northern Ireland

Tel **02870 341469**
24 hour tel **0345 111 222**
Minicom **02870 341 380**

www.dvlni.gov.uk

The theory test

Test overview

The theory test is a computer-based test and has a multiple-choice part followed by a hazard perception part. You need to pass both parts of the theory test at the same sitting to get your theory test pass certificate.

For the multiple-choice part, you choose your answers to 35 questions by simply touching the screen. The touch-screen system has been carefully designed to make it easy to use. You can practise for up to 15 minutes before the test starts, staff at the test centre will be on hand to help you if you have any difficulties. Only one question appears on the screen at a time and you select the answer by simply touching the screen. You can move backwards and forwards through the questions and go back to questions that you want to look at again.

shows the question number

shows your name and category of test

shows the time remaining, an icon will pop up when you have five minutes left

shows how many answers are required

shows the question

touch the screen to indicate which answer(s) are correct

touch this to go back to the previous page

touch this to move on to the next question

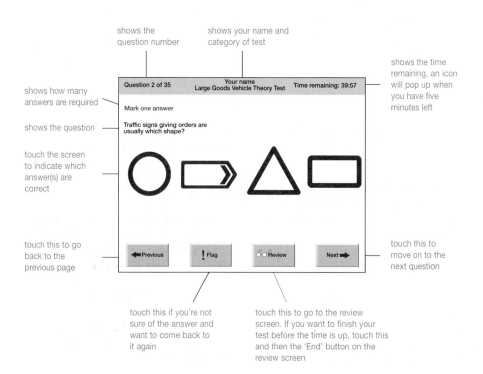

touch this if you're not sure of the answer and want to come back to it again

touch this to go to the review screen. If you want to finish your test before the time is up, touch this and then the 'End' button on the review screen

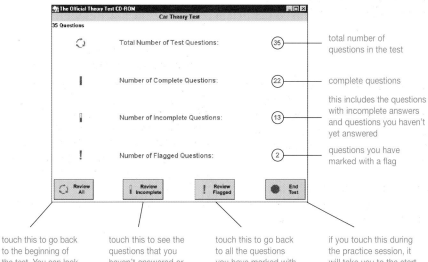

The Official Theory Test CD-ROM

Car Theory Test

35 Questions

○ Total Number of Test Questions:	35	total number of questions in the test
▌ Number of Complete Questions:	22	complete questions
▐ Number of Incomplete Questions:	13	this includes the questions with incomplete answers and questions you haven't yet answered
! Number of Flagged Questions:	2	questions you have marked with a flag

Review All | Review Incomplete | Review Flagged | End Test

touch this to go back to the beginning of the test. You can look at all questions again and change your answers if you want

touch this to see the questions that you haven't answered or have marked with the wrong number of answers

touch this to go back to all the questions you have marked with a flag. You can then work through all the flagged questions

if you touch this during the practice session, it will take you to the start of the test. During the actual test this button will end the test session

It's easy to change your answer - the system will alert you if you have not completely answered a question.

You will have 40 minutes to complete the multiple-choice part of the test and you must answer at least 30 questions correctly to pass.

Preparing for your test

All the questions you could be asked in the multiple choice part of the theory test are detailed in *The Official Theory Test for Car Drivers* book. It also includes an explanation of why each answer is correct.

The Official Theory Test for Car Drivers CD-Rom contains all this and also allows you to sit realistic mock exams and to create customised tests tailored to target your weaker areas.

The Official Guide to Hazard Perception DVD is the ideal way to prepare for the hazard perception part of the theory test. The fully interactive DVD contains clear guidance on how to recognise and respond to hazards on the road. It's packed with useful tips, quizzes, expert advice and includes official DSA hazard perception video clips with feedback on your performance.

Booking your theory test

Theory test centres

There are over 150 theory test centres throughout England, Scotland and Wales, and six in Northern Ireland. Most people have a test centre within 20 miles of their home, but this will vary depending on the density of population in your area.

Test centres are usually open on weekdays, some evenings and Saturdays.

The easiest ways to book your test are online or by phone, but you can also book by post.

Booking online or by telephone

By using these methods you'll be given the date and time of your test immediately. You can book online at www.dsa.gov.uk (for Northern Ireland use www.doeni.gov.uk/dvta)

To book by telephone, call 0870 0101 372 (0845 600 6700 for Northern Ireland) between 8am and 6pm Monday to Friday and 8am and 4pm on Saturdays.

If you're deaf and use a minicom machine, call 0870 0106 372 and if you are a Welsh speaker, call 0870 0100 372.

When booking your test you will need your

- DVLA or DVLNI driving licence number
- credit or debit card details. Please note that the person who books the test must be the card holder. We accept Mastercard, Visa, Delta, Switch and Solo.

You'll be given a booking number and sent an appointment letter that you should receive within eight days.

Booking by post

If you prefer to book by post, you'll need to fill in an application form. These are available from theory test centres or driving test centres, or your instructor may have one.

If you require a theory test in a language other than English or provision for special needs you must state your needs when you book your test.

You should normally receive an appointment letter within ten days of posting your application form.

Using the revision test papers

The revision papers in this book give you an opportunity to test yourself on paper before you take your test. The questions are graded just as they are in the real test, each paper includes a proportionate number taken from each section of the total bank of theory test questions.

You should study *The Official Theory Test for Car Drivers* before taking the sample tests on the following pages.

Instructions

For each question you must find the right answer (or answers) and circle the bullet (or bullets). The answers to the questions are given on p50-54.

To pass each test you must get 30 or more answers correct.

Don't forget that the real test has a time limit of 40 minutes for the multiple choice part.

The two samples below show how the questions should be completed. The number of answers that should be marked is shown on the right hand side of the bar at the top of each question:

| 3.37 | Mark **two** answers |

As a driver you can cause more damage to the environment by

⊙ choosing a fuel-efficient vehicle
◉ making a lot of short journeys
⊙ driving in as high a gear as possible
◉ accelerating as quickly as possible
⊙ having your vehicle regularly serviced

| 11.60 | Mark **one** answer |

What does this sign mean?

⊙ Cyclists must dismount
⊙ Cycles are not allowed
◉ Cycle route ahead
⊙ Cycle in single file

Revision paper one

1.1   *Mark **one** answer*

You are driving on a wet road. You have to stop your vehicle in an emergency. You should

⊙ apply the handbrake and footbrake together

⊙ keep both hands on the wheel

⊙ select reverse gear

⊙ give an arm signal

1.2   *Mark **one** answer*

Using front fog lights in clear daylight will

⊙ flatten the battery

⊙ dazzle other drivers

⊙ improve your visibility

⊙ increase your awareness

1.3   *Mark **one** answer*

You are towing a trailer on a motorway. What is your maximum speed limit?

⊙ 40 mph

⊙ 50 mph

⊙ 60 mph

⊙ 70 mph

1.4   *Mark **one** answer*

You see this sign at a crossroads. You should

⊙ maintain the same speed

⊙ carry on with great care

⊙ find another route

⊙ telephone the police

1.5   *Mark **one** answer*

At an accident it is important to look after the casualty. When the area is safe, you should

⊙ get them out of the vehicle

⊙ give them a drink

⊙ give them something to eat

⊙ keep them in the vehicle

1.6   *Mark **one** answer*

You arrive at the scene of an accident. A pedestrian is bleeding heavily from a leg wound but the leg is not broken. What should you do?

⊙ Dab the wound to stop the bleeding

⊙ Keep both legs flat on the ground

⊙ Apply firm pressure to the wound

⊙ Fetch them a warm drink

1.7   *Mark **one** answer*

When parking and leaving your car
you should

- ⊙ park under a shady tree
- ⊙ remove the tax disc
- ⊙ park in a quiet road
- ⊙ engage the steering lock

1.8   *Mark **one** answer*

On a vehicle, where would you find a
catalytic converter?

- ⊙ In the fuel tank
- ⊙ In the air filter
- ⊙ On the cooling system
- ⊙ On the exhaust system

1.9   *Mark **three** answers*

You have third party insurance. What does
this cover?

- ⊙ Damage to your own vehicle
- ⊙ Damage to your vehicle by fire
- ⊙ Injury to another person
- ⊙ Damage to someone's property
- ⊙ Damage to other vehicles
- ⊙ Injury to yourself

1.10   *Mark **one** answer*

You are braking on a wet road. Your vehicle
begins to skid. It does not have anti-lock
brakes. What is the FIRST thing you
should do?

- ⊙ Quickly pull up the handbrake
- ⊙ Release the footbrake fully
- ⊙ Push harder on the brake pedal
- ⊙ Gently use the accelerator

1.11   *Mark **one** answer*

What does this sign mean?

- ⊙ Two-way traffic ahead across a
  one-way road
- ⊙ Traffic approaching you has priority
- ⊙ Two-way traffic straight ahead
- ⊙ Motorway contraflow system ahead

1.12   *Mark **one** answer*

Which is a hazard warning line?

What does this sign tell you?

- That it is a no-through road
- End of traffic calming zone
- Free parking zone ends
- No waiting zone ends

You are approaching a zebra crossing where pedestrians are waiting. Which arm signal might you give?

Anti-lock brakes can greatly assist with

- a higher cruising speed
- steering control when braking
- control when accelerating
- motorway driving

What is the reason for the area marked in red and white along the centre of this road?

- It is to separate traffic flowing in opposite directions
- It marks an area to be used by overtaking motorcyclists
- It is a temporary marking to warn of the roadworks
- It is separating the two sides of the dual carriageway

To help keep your vehicle secure at night, where should you park?

- Near a police station
- In a quiet road
- On a red route
- In a well-lit area

On a road where trams operate, which of these vehicles will be most at risk from the tram rails?

- Cars
- Cycles
- Buses
- Lorries

1.19 *Mark **one** answer*

Where would you see this sign?

- Near a school crossing
- At a playground entrance
- On a school bus
- At a 'pedestrians only' area

1.20 *Mark **one** answer*

There are flashing amber lights under a school warning sign. What action should you take?

- Reduce speed until you are clear of the area
- Keep up your speed and sound the horn
- Increase your speed to clear the area quickly
- Wait at the lights until they change to green

1.21 *Mark **three** answers*

To avoid an accident when entering a contraflow system, you should

- reduce speed in good time
- switch lanes any time to make progress
- choose an appropriate lane early
- keep the correct separation distance
- increase speed to pass through quickly
- follow other motorists closely to avoid long queues

1.22 *Mark **one** answer*

You want to turn right from a main road into a side road. Just before turning you should

- cancel your right-turn signal
- select first gear
- check for traffic overtaking on your right
- stop and set the handbrake

1.23 *Mark **one** answer*

A single carriageway road has this sign. What is the maximum permitted speed for a car towing a trailer?

- 30 mph
- 40 mph
- 50 mph
- 60 mph

1.24 *Mark **one** answer*

Some two-way roads are divided into three lanes. Why are these particularly dangerous?

- Traffic in both directions can use the middle lane to overtake
- Traffic can travel faster in poor weather conditions
- Traffic can overtake on the left
- Traffic uses the middle lane for emergencies only

1.25

Turning the steering wheel while your car is stationary can cause damage to the

- ⊙ gearbox
- ⊙ engine
- ⊙ brakes
- ⊙ steering
- ⊙ tyres

1.26

Before overtaking a large vehicle you should keep well back. Why is this?

- ⊙ To give acceleration space to overtake quickly on blind bends
- ⊙ To get the best view of the road ahead
- ⊙ To leave a gap in case the vehicle stops and rolls back
- ⊙ To offer other drivers a safe gap if they want to overtake you

1.27

Your vehicle has broken down on a motorway. You are not able to stop on the hard shoulder. What should you do?

- ⊙ Switch on your hazard warning lights
- ⊙ Stop following traffic and ask for help
- ⊙ Attempt to repair your vehicle quickly
- ⊙ Stand behind your vehicle to warn others

1.28

You are travelling at night. You are dazzled by headlights coming towards you. You should

- ⊙ pull down your sun visor
- ⊙ slow down or stop
- ⊙ switch on your main beam headlights
- ⊙ put your hand over your eyes

1.29

Why should the junction on the left be kept clear?

- ⊙ To allow vehicles to enter and emerge
- ⊙ To allow the bus to reverse
- ⊙ To allow vehicles to make a 'U' turn
- ⊙ To allow vehicles to park

1.30

Car passengers MUST wear a seat belt if one is available, unless they are

- ⊙ under 14 years old
- ⊙ under 1.5 metres (5 feet) in height
- ⊙ sitting in the rear seat
- ⊙ exempt for medical reasons

1.31 *Mark **one** answer*

It is very windy. You are behind a motorcyclist who is overtaking a high-sided vehicle. What should you do?

- ⊙ Overtake the motorcyclist immediately
- ⊙ Keep well back
- ⊙ Stay level with the motorcyclist
- ⊙ Keep close to the motorcyclist

1.32 *Mark **one** answer*

When approaching this bridge you should give way to

- ⊙ bicycles
- ⊙ buses
- ⊙ motorcycles
- ⊙ cars

1.33 *Mark **one** answer*

A child under three years is being carried in your vehicle. They should be secured in a restraint. Which of these is suitable?

- ⊙ An adult holding a child
- ⊙ A lap belt
- ⊙ A baby carrier
- ⊙ An adult seat belt

1.34 *Mark **one** answer*

You are driving in slow-moving queues of traffic. Just before changing lane you should

- ⊙ sound the horn
- ⊙ look for motorcyclists filtering through the traffic
- ⊙ give a 'slowing down' arm signal
- ⊙ change down to first gear

1.35 *Mark **one** answer*

You are approaching a pelican crossing. The amber light is flashing. You must

- ⊙ give way to pedestrians who are crossing
- ⊙ encourage pedestrians to cross
- ⊙ not move until the green light appears
- ⊙ stop even if the crossing is clear

Revision paper two

2.1
*Mark **one** answer*

Your motor insurance policy has an excess of £100. What does this mean?

- The insurance company will pay the first £100 of any claim
- You will be paid £100 if you do not have an accident
- Your vehicle is insured for a value of £100 if it is stolen
- You will have to pay the first £100 of any claim

2.2
*Mark **one** answer*

Why is passing a lorry more risky than passing a car?

- Lorries are longer than cars
- Lorries may suddenly pull up
- The brakes of lorries are not as good
- Lorries climb hills more slowly

2.3
*Mark **one** answer*

What does this sign mean?

- End of dual carriageway
- Tall bridge
- Road narrows
- End of narrow bridge

2.4
*Mark **one** answer*

What does this sign mean?

- Turn left for parking area
- No through road on the left
- No entry for traffic turning left
- Turn left for ferry terminal

2.5
*Mark **one** answer*

What advice should you give to a driver who has had a few alcoholic drinks at a party?

- Have a strong cup of coffee and then drive home
- Drive home carefully and slowly
- Go home by public transport
- Wait a short while and then drive home

2.6
*Mark **one** answer*

You are travelling on a well-lit road at night in a built-up area. By using dipped headlights you will be able to

- see further along the road
- go at a much faster speed
- switch to main beam quickly
- be easily seen by others

2.7   Mark **four** answers

Which FOUR of these must NOT use motorways?

- ⊙ Learner car drivers
- ⊙ Motorcycles over 50cc
- ⊙ Double-deck buses
- ⊙ Farm tractors
- ⊙ Learner motorcyclists
- ⊙ Cyclists

2.8   Mark **one** answer

A long, heavily-laden lorry is taking a long time to overtake you. What should you do?

- ⊙ Speed up
- ⊙ Slow down
- ⊙ Hold your speed
- ⊙ Change direction

2.9   Mark **one** answer

What is the main hazard the driver of the red car (arrowed) should be aware of?

- ⊙ Glare from the sun may affect the driver's vision
- ⊙ The black car may stop suddenly
- ⊙ The bus may move out into the road
- ⊙ Oncoming vehicles will assume the driver is turning right

2.10   Mark **one** answer

You have just gone through deep water. To dry off the brakes you should

- ⊙ accelerate and keep to a high speed for a short time
- ⊙ go slowly while gently applying the brakes
- ⊙ avoid using the brakes at all for a few miles
- ⊙ stop for at least an hour to allow them time to dry

2.11   Mark **one** answer

What colour are the reflective studs between a motorway and its slip road?

- ⊙ Amber
- ⊙ White
- ⊙ Green
- ⊙ Red

2.12   Mark **one** answer

You find that you need glasses to read vehicle number plates at the required distance. When MUST you wear them?

- ⊙ Only in bad weather conditions
- ⊙ At all times when driving
- ⊙ Only when you think it necessary
- ⊙ Only in bad light or at night time

Where is the safest place to park your vehicle at night?

- ⊙ In a garage
- ⊙ On a busy road
- ⊙ In a quiet car park
- ⊙ Near a red route

You are approaching a zebra crossing. Pedestrians are waiting to cross. You should

- ⊙ give way to the elderly and infirm only
- ⊙ slow down and prepare to stop
- ⊙ use your headlights to indicate they can cross
- ⊙ wave at them to cross the road

You are driving with your front fog lights switched on. Earlier fog has now cleared. What should you do?

- ⊙ Leave them on if other drivers have their lights on
- ⊙ Switch them off as long as visibility remains good
- ⊙ Flash them to warn oncoming traffic that it is foggy
- ⊙ Drive with them on instead of your headlights

An injured motorcyclist is lying unconscious in the road. You should

- ⊙ remove the safety helmet
- ⊙ seek medical assistance
- ⊙ move the person off the road
- ⊙ remove the leather jacket

You are following a long vehicle. It approaches a crossroads and signals left, but moves out to the right. You should

- ⊙ get closer in order to pass it quickly
- ⊙ stay well back and give it room
- ⊙ assume the signal is wrong and it is really turning right
- ⊙ overtake as it starts to slow down

You are driving along a motorway and become tired. You should

- ⊙ stop at the next service area and rest
- ⊙ leave the motorway at the next exit and rest
- ⊙ increase your speed and turn up the radio volume
- ⊙ close all your windows and set heating to warm
- ⊙ pull up on the hard shoulder and change drivers

2.19   *Mark **three** answers*

At road junctions which of the following are most vulnerable?

- ⊙ Cyclists
- ⊙ Motorcyclists
- ⊙ Pedestrians
- ⊙ Car drivers
- ⊙ Lorry drivers

2.20   *Mark **one** answer*

You are following two cyclists. They approach a roundabout in the left-hand lane. In which direction should you expect the cyclists to go?

- ⊙ Left
- ⊙ Right
- ⊙ Any direction
- ⊙ Straight ahead

2.21   *Mark **one** answer*

What does this traffic sign mean?

- ⊙ Slippery road ahead
- ⊙ Tyres liable to punctures ahead
- ⊙ Danger ahead
- ⊙ Service area ahead

2.22   *Mark **four** answers*

Before starting a journey in freezing weather you should clear ice and snow from your vehicle's

- ⊙ aerial
- ⊙ windows
- ⊙ bumper
- ⊙ lights
- ⊙ mirrors
- ⊙ number plates

2.23   *Mark **one** answer*

You arrive at an accident. A motorcyclist is unconscious. Your FIRST priority is the casualty's

- ⊙ breathing
- ⊙ bleeding
- ⊙ broken bones
- ⊙ bruising

2.24   *Mark **one** answer*

You are turning left into a side road. Pedestrians are crossing the road near the junction. You must

- ⊙ wave them on
- ⊙ sound your horn
- ⊙ switch on your hazard lights
- ⊙ wait for them to cross

What does this sign mean?

- ◉ The right-hand lane ahead is narrow
- ◉ Right-hand lane for buses only
- ◉ Right-hand lane for turning right
- ◉ The right-hand lane is closed

A red traffic light means

- ◉ you should stop unless turning left
- ◉ stop, if you are able to brake safely
- ◉ you must stop and wait behind the stop line
- ◉ proceed with caution

You have to leave valuables in your car. It would be safer to

- ◉ put them in a carrier bag
- ◉ park near a school entrance
- ◉ lock them out of sight
- ◉ park near a bus stop

When emerging from junctions, which is most likely to obstruct your view?

- ◉ Windscreen pillars
- ◉ Steering wheel
- ◉ Interior mirror
- ◉ Windscreen wipers

You are on a motorway at night. You MUST have your headlights switched on unless

- ◉ there are vehicles close in front of you
- ◉ you are travelling below 50 mph
- ◉ the motorway is lit
- ◉ your vehicle is broken down on the hard shoulder

You are the first person to arrive at an accident where people are badly injured. Which THREE should you do?

- ◉ Switch on your own hazard warning lights
- ◉ Make sure that someone telephones for an ambulance
- ◉ Try and get people who are injured to drink something
- ◉ Move the people who are injured clear of their vehicles
- ◉ Get people who are not injured clear of the scene

2.31
*Mark **two** answers*

Excessive or uneven tyre wear can be caused by faults in the

- gearbox
- braking system
- suspension
- exhaust system

2.32
*Mark **one** answer*

Driving at 70 mph uses more fuel than driving at 50 mph by up to

- 10%
- 30%
- 75%
- 100%

2.33
*Mark **three** answers*

On which THREE occasions MUST you stop your vehicle?

- When in an accident were damage or injury is caused
- At a red traffic light
- When signalled to do so by a police officer
- At a junction with double broken white lines
- At a pelican crossing when the amber light is flashing and no pedestrians are crossing

2.34
*Mark **three** answers*

Which THREE of the following are most likely to waste fuel?

- Reducing your speed
- Carrying unnecessary weight
- Using the wrong grade of fuel
- Under-inflated tyres
- Using different brands of fuel
- A fitted, empty roof rack

2.35
*Mark **two** answers*

Overloading your vehicle can seriously affect the

- gearbox
- steering
- handling
- battery life
- journey time

Revision paper three

You have stopped at the scene of an accident to give help. Which THREE things should you do?

- ⊙ Keep injured people warm and comfortable
- ⊙ Keep injured people calm by talking to them reassuringly
- ⊙ Keep injured people on the move by walking them around
- ⊙ Give injured people a warm drink
- ⊙ Make sure that injured people are not left alone

Wherever possible, which one of the following should you do when parking at night?

- ⊙ Park in a quiet car park
- ⊙ Park in a well-lit area
- ⊙ Park facing against the flow of traffic
- ⊙ Park next to a busy junction

What is the national speed limit for cars and motorcycles on a dual carriageway?

- ⊙ 30 mph
- ⊙ 50 mph
- ⊙ 60 mph
- ⊙ 70 mph

You are driving the children of a friend home from school. They are both under 14 years old. Who is responsible for making sure they wear a seat belt?

- ⊙ An adult passenger
- ⊙ The children
- ⊙ You, the driver
- ⊙ Your friend

What shape is a STOP sign at a junction?

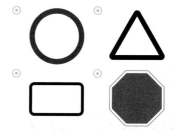

Daytime visibility is poor but not seriously reduced. You should switch on

- ⊙ headlights and fog lights
- ⊙ front fog lights
- ⊙ dipped headlights
- ⊙ rear fog lights

3.7
*Mark **one** answer*

When may you NOT overtake on the left?

- ⊙ On a free-flowing motorway or dual carriageway
- ⊙ When the traffic is moving slowly in queues
- ⊙ On a one-way street
- ⊙ When the car in front is signalling to turn right

3.8
*Mark **one** answer*

This marking appears on the road just before a

- ⊙ 'no entry' sign
- ⊙ 'give way' sign
- ⊙ 'stop' sign
- ⊙ 'no through road' sign

3.9
*Mark **one** answer*

These road markings must be kept clear
to allow

- ⊙ school children to be dropped off
- ⊙ for teachers to park
- ⊙ school children to be picked up
- ⊙ a clear view of the crossing area

3.10
*Mark **one** answer*

Anti-lock brakes prevent wheels from locking. This means the tyres are less likely to

- ⊙ aquaplane
- ⊙ skid
- ⊙ puncture
- ⊙ wear

3.11
*Mark **one** answer*

What is the main hazard shown in this picture?

- ⊙ Vehicles turning right
- ⊙ Vehicles doing U-turns
- ⊙ The cyclist crossing the road
- ⊙ Parked cars around the corner

3.12
*Mark **one** answer*

What does this sign mean?

- ⊙ No footpath ahead
- ⊙ Pedestrians only ahead
- ⊙ Pedestrian crossing ahead
- ⊙ School crossing ahead

Why is it dangerous to leave rear fog lights on when they are not needed?

- Brake lights are less clear
- Following drivers can be dazzled
- Electrical systems could be overloaded
- Direction indicators may not work properly
- The battery could fail

Which THREE of the following do you need before you can drive legally?

- A valid driving licence with signature
- A valid tax disc displayed on your vehicle
- A vehicle service record
- Proper insurance cover
- Breakdown cover
- A vehicle handbook

Which of these IS NOT allowed to travel in the right-hand lane of a three-lane motorway?

- A small delivery van
- A motorcycle
- A vehicle towing a trailer
- A motorcycle and side-car

You are driving over a level crossing. The warning lights come on and a bell rings. What should you do?

- Get everyone out of the vehicle immediately
- Stop and reverse back to clear the crossing
- Keep going and clear the crossing
- Stop immediately and use your hazard warning lights

A cycle lane is marked by a solid white line. You must not drive or park in it

- at any time
- during the rush hour
- if a cyclist is using it
- during its period of operation

What type of emergency vehicle is fitted with a green flashing beacon?

- Fire engine
- Road gritter
- Ambulance
- Doctor's car

3.19 *Mark one answer*

There has been an accident. A motorcyclist is lying injured and unconscious. Why should you usually not attempt to remove their helmet?

- Because they may not want you to
- This could result in more serious injury
- They will get too cold if you do this
- Because you could scratch the helmet

3.20 *Mark one answer*

You are approaching crossroads. The traffic lights have failed. What should you do?

- Brake and stop only for large vehicles
- Brake sharply to a stop before looking
- Be prepared to brake sharply to a stop
- Be prepared to stop for any traffic.

3.21 *Mark one answer*

How could you deter theft from your car when leaving it unattended?

- Leave valuables in a carrier bag
- Lock valuables out of sight
- Put valuables on the seats
- Leave valuables on the floor

3.22 *Mark two answers*

Which TWO things would help to keep you alert during a long journey?

- Finishing your journey as fast as you can
- Keeping off the motorways and using country roads
- Making sure that you get plenty of fresh air
- Making regular stops for refreshments

3.23 *Mark one answer*

At a pelican crossing the flashing amber light means you MUST

- stop and wait for the green light
- stop and wait for the red light
- give way to pedestrians waiting to cross
- give way to pedestrians already on the crossing

3.24 *Mark two answers*

Anti-lock brakes may not work as effectively if the road surface is

- dry
- loose
- wet
- good
- firm

3.25   *Mark one answer*

The left-hand pavement is closed due to street repairs. What should you do?

- ⊙ Watch out for pedestrians walking in the road
- ⊙ Use your right-hand mirror more often
- ⊙ Speed up to get past the roadworks quicker
- ⊙ Position close to the left-hand kerb

3.26   *Mark one answer*

You are travelling along this narrow country road. When passing the cyclist you should go

- ⊙ slowly, sounding the horn as you pass
- ⊙ quickly, leaving plenty of room
- ⊙ slowly, leaving plenty of room
- ⊙ quickly, sounding the horn as you pass

3.27   *Mark one answer*

Why should you make sure that your indicators are cancelled after turning?

- ⊙ To avoid flattening the battery
- ⊙ To avoid misleading other road users
- ⊙ To avoid dazzling other road users
- ⊙ To avoid damage to the indicator relay

3.28   *Mark one answer*

When should you especially check the engine oil level?

- ⊙ Before a long journey
- ⊙ When the engine is hot
- ⊙ Early in the morning
- ⊙ Every 6000 miles

3.29   *Mark one answer*

Why is it particularly important to carry out a check on your vehicle before making a long motorway journey?

- ⊙ You will have to do more harsh braking on motorways
- ⊙ Motorway service stations do not deal with breakdowns
- ⊙ The road surface will wear down the tyres faster
- ⊙ Continuous high speeds may increase the risk of your vehicle breaking down

3.30   *Mark one answer*

You start to feel tired while driving. What should you do?

- ⊙ Increase your speed slightly
- ⊙ Decrease your speed slightly
- ⊙ Find a less busy route
- ⊙ Pull over at a safe place to rest

3.31   *Mark **two** answers*

You are towing a small trailer on a busy three-lane motorway. All the lanes are open. You must

- ⊙ not exceed 60 mph
- ⊙ not overtake
- ⊙ have a stabiliser fitted
- ⊙ use only the left and centre lanes

3.32   *Mark **one** answer*

There is a slow-moving motorcyclist ahead of you. You are unsure what the rider is going to do. You should

- ⊙ pass on the left
- ⊙ pass on the right
- ⊙ stay behind
- ⊙ move closer

3.33   *Mark **one** answer*

You see a pedestrian with a dog. The dog has a bright orange lead and collar. This especially warns you that the pedestrian is

- ⊙ elderly
- ⊙ dog training
- ⊙ colour blind
- ⊙ deaf

3.34   *Mark **one** answer*

You are following a long lorry. The driver signals to turn left into a narrow road. What should you do?

- ⊙ Overtake on the left before the lorry reaches the junction
- ⊙ Overtake on the right as soon as the lorry slows down
- ⊙ Do not overtake unless you can see there is no oncoming traffic
- ⊙ Do not overtake, stay well back and be prepared to stop.

3.35   *Mark **one** answer*

What should you do as you approach this lorry?

- ⊙ Slow down and be prepared to wait
- ⊙ Make the lorry wait for you
- ⊙ Flash your lights at the lorry
- ⊙ Move to the right-hand side of the road

Revision paper four

4.1   Mark **one** answer

A crawler lane on a motorway is found

- ⊙ on a steep gradient
- ⊙ before a service area
- ⊙ before a junction
- ⊙ along the hard shoulder

4.4   Mark **one** answer

Where would you see these road markings?

- ⊙ At a level crossing
- ⊙ On a motorway slip road
- ⊙ At a pedestrian crossing
- ⊙ On a single-track road

4.2   Mark **one** answer

What does this sign tell you?

- ⊙ No cycling
- ⊙ Cycle route ahead
- ⊙ Route for cycles only
- ⊙ End of cycle route

4.5   Mark **one** answer

You have been involved in an argument before starting your journey. This has made you feel angry. You should

- ⊙ start to drive, but open a window
- ⊙ drive slower than normal and turn your radio on
- ⊙ have an alcoholic drink to help you relax before driving
- ⊙ calm down before you start to drive

4.3   Mark **one** answer

When leaving your car to help keep it secure you should

- ⊙ leave the hazard warning lights on
- ⊙ lock it and remove the key
- ⊙ park on a one-way street
- ⊙ park in a residential area

4.6   Mark **one** answer

New petrol-engined cars must be fitted with catalytic converters. The reason for this is to

- ⊙ control exhaust noise levels
- ⊙ prolong the life of the exhaust system
- ⊙ allow the exhaust system to be recycled
- ⊙ reduce harmful exhaust emissions

4.7   *Mark **one** answer*

It is essential that tyre pressures are checked regularly. When should this be done?

- After any lengthy journey
- After travelling at high speed
- When tyres are hot
- When tyres are cold

4.8   *Mark **one** answer*

You are on a motorway. A large box falls onto the road from a lorry. The lorry does not stop. You should

- go to the next emergency telephone and inform the police
- catch up with the lorry and try to get the driver's attention
- stop close to the box until the police arrive
- pull over to the hard shoulder, then remove the box

4.9   *Mark **one** answer*

What do these zigzag lines at pedestrian crossings mean?

- No parking at any time
- Parking allowed only for a short time
- Slow down to 20 mph
- Sounding horns is not allowed

4.10   *Mark **one** answer*

You are approaching this roundabout and see the cyclist signal right. Why is the cyclist keeping to the left?

- It is a quicker route for the cyclist
- The cyclist is going to turn left instead
- The cyclist thinks *The Highway Code* does not apply to bicycles
- The cyclist is slower and more vulnerable

4.11   *Mark **one** answer*

Which of the following may reduce the cost of your insurance?

- Having a valid MOT certificate
- Taking a Pass Plus course
- Driving a powerful car
- Having penalty points on your licence

4.12   *Mark **one** answer*

Your mobile phone rings while you are on the motorway. Before answering you should

- reduce your speed to 30 mph
- pull up on the hard shoulder
- move into the left-hand lane
- stop in a safe place

At this junction there is a stop sign with a solid white line on the road surface. Why is there a stop sign here?

- ⊙ Speed on the major road is de-restricted
- ⊙ It is a busy junction
- ⊙ Visibility along the major road is restricted
- ⊙ There are hazard warning lines in the centre of the road

As a provisional licence holder, you must not drive a motor car

- ⊙ at more than 40 mph
- ⊙ on your own
- ⊙ on the motorway
- ⊙ under the age of 18 years at night
- ⊙ with passengers in the rear seats

Where on a motorway would you find green reflective studs?

- ⊙ Separating driving lanes
- ⊙ Between the hard shoulder and the carriageway
- ⊙ At slip road entrances and exits
- ⊙ Between the carriageway and the central reservation

You are driving along this road. What should you be prepared to do?

- ⊙ Sound your horn and continue
- ⊙ Slow down and give way
- ⊙ Report the driver to the police
- ⊙ Squeeze through the gap

When leaving your vehicle parked and unattended you should

- ⊙ park near a busy junction
- ⊙ park in a housing estate
- ⊙ remove the key and lock it
- ⊙ leave the left indicator on

Which sign means 'two-way traffic crosses a one-way road'?

4.19   *Mark **one** answer*

You are on a motorway at night with other vehicles just ahead of you. Which lights should you have on?

- ⊙ Front fog lights
- ⊙ Main beam headlights
- ⊙ Sidelights only
- ⊙ Dipped headlights

4.20   *Mark **two** answers*

On which TWO occasions might you inflate your tyres to more than the recommended normal pressure?

- ⊙ When the roads are slippery
- ⊙ When driving fast for a long distance
- ⊙ When the tyre tread is worn below 2mm
- ⊙ When carrying a heavy load
- ⊙ When the weather is cold
- ⊙ When the vehicle is fitted with anti-lock brakes

4.21   *Mark **one** answer*

The red lights are flashing. What should you do when approaching this level crossing?

- ⊙ Go through quickly
- ⊙ Go through carefully
- ⊙ Stop before the barrier
- ⊙ Switch on hazard warning lights

4.22   *Mark **one** answer*

You are on a motorway. You feel tired. You should

- ⊙ carry on but go slowly
- ⊙ leave the motorway at the next exit
- ⊙ complete your journey as quickly as possible
- ⊙ stop on the hard shoulder

4.23   *Mark **one** answer*

You are travelling at 50 mph on a good, dry road. What is your shortest overall stopping distance?

- ⊙ 36 metres (120 feet)
- ⊙ 53 metres (175 feet)
- ⊙ 75 metres (245 feet)
- ⊙ 96 metres (315 feet)

4.24   *Mark **one** answer*

Your car is fitted with anti-lock brakes. You need to stop in an emergency. You should

- ⊙ brake normally and avoid turning the steering wheel
- ⊙ press the brake pedal promptly and firmly until you have stopped
- ⊙ keep pushing and releasing the foot brake quickly to prevent skidding
- ⊙ apply the handbrake to reduce the stopping distance

What does this sign mean?

- Contraflow pedal cycle lane
- With-flow pedal cycle lane
- Pedal cycles and buses only
- No pedal cycles or buses

You park overnight on a road with a 40 mph speed limit. You should park

- facing the traffic
- with parking lights on
- with dipped headlights on
- near a street light

You are following other vehicles in fog with your lights on. How else can you reduce the chances of being involved in an accident?

- Keep close to the vehicle in front
- Use your main beam instead of dipped headlights
- Keep together with the faster vehicles
- Reduce your speed and increase the gap

A person herding sheep asks you to stop. You should

- ignore them as they have no authority
- stop and switch off your engine
- continue on but drive slowly
- try and get past quickly

You are following a large articulated vehicle. It is going to turn left into a narrow road. What action should you take?

- Move out and overtake on the right
- Pass on the left as the vehicle moves out
- Be prepared to stop behind
- Overtake quickly before the lorry moves out

When may you reverse from a side road into a main road?

- Only if both roads are clear of traffic
- Not at any time
- At any time
- Only if the main road is clear of traffic

4.31 *Mark **one** answer*

You have a collision whilst your car is moving. What is the first thing you must do?

- ⊙ Stop only if there are injured people
- ⊙ Call the emergency services
- ⊙ Stop at the scene of the accident
- ⊙ Call your insurance company

4.32 *Mark **one** answer*

You should leave at least a two-second gap between your vehicle and the one in front when conditions are

- ⊙ wet
- ⊙ good
- ⊙ damp
- ⊙ foggy

4.33 *Mark **one** answer*

You are approaching a busy junction. There are several lanes with road markings. At the last moment you realise that you are in the wrong lane. You should

- ⊙ continue in that lane
- ⊙ force your way across
- ⊙ stop until the area has cleared
- ⊙ use clear arm signals to cut across

4.34 *Mark **one** answer*

You are driving at 70 mph on a three-lane motorway. There is no traffic ahead. Which lane should you use?

- ⊙ Any lane
- ⊙ Middle lane
- ⊙ Right lane
- ⊙ Left lane

4.35 *Mark **one** answer*

You have broken down on a two-way road. You have a warning triangle. It should be displayed

- ⊙ on the roof of your vehicle
- ⊙ at least 150 metres (492 feet) behind your vehicle
- ⊙ at least 45 metres (147 feet) behind your vehicle
- ⊙ just behind your vehicle

Revision paper five

What do these motorway signs show?

⊙ They are countdown markers to a bridge

⊙ They are distance markers to the next telephone

⊙ They are countdown markers to the next exit

⊙ They warn of a police control ahead

To supervise a learner driver you must

⊙ have held a full licence for at least 3 years

⊙ be at least 21 years old

⊙ be an approved driving instructor

⊙ hold an advanced driving certificate

Who has priority at an unmarked crossroads?

⊙ The larger vehicle

⊙ No one has priority

⊙ The faster vehicle

⊙ The smaller vehicle

Why are vehicles fitted with rear fog lights?

⊙ To be seen when driving at high speed

⊙ To use if broken down in a dangerous position

⊙ To make them more visible in thick fog

⊙ To warn drivers following closely to drop back

What does this sign mean?

⊙ Roundabout

⊙ Crossroads

⊙ No stopping

⊙ No entry

When going straight ahead at a roundabout you should

⊙ indicate left before leaving the roundabout

⊙ not indicate at any time

⊙ indicate right when approaching the roundabout

⊙ indicate left when approaching the roundabout

5.7 _Mark **one** answer_

What does this sign mean?

- Ring road
- Mini-roundabout
- No vehicles
- Roundabout

5.8 _Mark **two** answers_

During periods of illness your ability to drive may be impaired. You MUST

- see your doctor each time before you drive
- only take smaller doses of any medicines
- be medically fit to drive
- not drive after taking certain medicines
- take all your medicines with you when you drive

5.9 _Mark **one** answer_

As a provisional licence holder you should not drive a car

- over 30 mph
- at night
- on the motorway
- with passengers in rear seats

5.10 _Mark **one** answer_

What does this sign mean?

- Motorcycles only
- No cars
- Cars only
- No motorcycles

5.11 _Mark **one** answer_

Which sign means no motor vehicles are allowed?

5.12 _Mark **one** answer_

When driving through a tunnel you should

- Look out for variable message signs
- Use your air conditioning system
- Switch on your rear fog lights
- Always use your windscreen wipers

*Mark **one** answer*

What is the purpose of these yellow criss-cross lines on the road?

- ⊙ To make you more aware of the traffic lights
- ⊙ To guide you into position as you turn
- ⊙ To prevent the junction becoming blocked
- ⊙ To show you where to stop when the lights change

5.14 *Mark **one** answer*

You may remove your seat belt when carrying out a manoeuvre that involves

- ⊙ reversing
- ⊙ a hill start
- ⊙ an emergency stop
- ⊙ driving slowly

5.15 *Mark **one** answer*

You are driving down a steep hill. Why could keeping the clutch down or rolling in neutral for too long be dangerous?

- ⊙ Fuel consumption will be higher
- ⊙ Your vehicle will pick up speed
- ⊙ It will damage the engine
- ⊙ It will wear tyres out more quickly

5.16 *Mark **one** answer*

You are turning left into a side road. What hazards should you be especially aware of?

- ⊙ One way street
- ⊙ Pedestrians
- ⊙ Traffic congestion
- ⊙ Parked vehicles

5.17 *Mark **one** answer*

In areas where there are 'traffic calming' measures you should

- ⊙ travel at a reduced speed
- ⊙ always travel at the speed limit
- ⊙ position in the centre of the road
- ⊙ only slow down if pedestrians are near

5.18 *Mark **one** answer*

You are reversing around a corner when you notice a pedestrian walking behind you. What should you do?

- ⊙ Slow down and wave the pedestrian across
- ⊙ Continue reversing and steer round the pedestrian
- ⊙ Stop and give way
- ⊙ Continue reversing and sound your horn

5.19

While driving, a warning light on your vehicle's instrument panel comes on. You should

- ⊙ continue if the engine sounds all right
- ⊙ hope that it is just a temporary electrical fault
- ⊙ deal with the problem when there is more time
- ⊙ check out the problem quickly and safely

5.20

You are driving towards a zebra crossing. A person in a wheelchair is waiting to cross. What should you do?

- ⊙ Continue on your way
- ⊙ Wave to the person to cross
- ⊙ Wave to the person to wait
- ⊙ Be prepared to stop

5.21

Your indicators may be difficult to see in bright sunlight. What should you do?

- ⊙ Put your indicator on earlier
- ⊙ Give an arm signal as well as using your indicator
- ⊙ Touch the brake several times to show the stop lights
- ⊙ Turn as quickly as you can

5.22

You are following a motorcyclist on an uneven road. You should

- ⊙ allow less room so you can be seen in their mirrors
- ⊙ overtake immediately
- ⊙ allow extra room in case they swerve to avoid potholes
- ⊙ allow the same room as normal because road surfaces do not affect motorcyclists

5.23

Your vehicle is fitted with a hand-held telephone. To use the telephone you should

- ⊙ reduce your speed
- ⊙ find a safe place to stop
- ⊙ steer the vehicle with one hand
- ⊙ be particularly careful at junctions

5.24

How can you stop a caravan snaking from side to side?

- ⊙ Turn the steering wheel slowly to each side
- ⊙ Accelerate to increase your speed
- ⊙ Stop as quickly as you can
- ⊙ Slow down very gradually

You are driving along a country road.
A horse and rider are approaching. What
should you do?

- Increase your speed
- Sound your horn
- Flash your headlights
- Drive slowly past
- Give plenty of room
- Rev your engine

How can you, as a driver, help the
environment?

- By reducing your speed
- By gentle acceleration
- By using leaded fuel
- By driving faster
- By harsh acceleration
- By servicing your vehicle properly

To reduce the volume of traffic on the
roads you could

- use public transport more often
- share a car when possible
- walk or cycle on short journeys
- travel by car at all times
- use a car with a smaller engine
- drive in a bus lane

Which of the following may help to deter a
thief from stealing your car?

- Always keeping the headlights on
- Fitting reflective glass windows
- Always keeping the interior light on
- Etching the car number on the windows

A bus lane on your left shows no times of
operation. This means it is

- not in operation at all
- only in operation at peak times
- in operation 24 hours a day
- only in operation in daylight hours

What THREE things should the driver of the
grey car (arrowed) be especially aware of?

- Pedestrians stepping out between cars
- Other cars behind the grey car
- Doors opening on parked cars
- The bumpy road surface
- Cars leaving parking spaces
- Empty parking spaces

5.31
*Mark **one** answer*

What should you do when leaving your vehicle?

- ⊙ Put valuable documents under the seats
- ⊙ Remove all valuables
- ⊙ Cover valuables with a blanket
- ⊙ Leave the interior light on

5.32
*Mark **one** answer*

You have just been overtaken by this motorcyclist who is cutting in sharply. You should

- ⊙ sound the horn
- ⊙ brake firmly
- ⊙ keep a safe gap
- ⊙ flash your lights

5.33
*Mark **one** answer*

You are on a wet motorway with surface spray. You should use

- ⊙ hazard flashers
- ⊙ dipped headlights
- ⊙ rear fog lights
- ⊙ sidelights

5.34
*Mark **one** answer*

You are about to overtake a slow-moving motorcyclist. Which one of these signs would make you take special care?

5.35
*Mark **one** answer*

As a driver why should you be more careful where trams operate?

- ⊙ Because they do not have a horn
- ⊙ Because they do not stop for cars
- ⊙ Because they do not have lights
- ⊙ Because they cannot steer to avoid you

37

Revision paper six

There is a tractor ahead of you. You wish to overtake but you are NOT sure if it is safe to do so. You should

- follow another overtaking vehicle through
- sound your horn to the slow vehicle to pull over
- speed through but flash your lights to oncoming traffic
- not overtake if you are in doubt

An accident has just happened. An injured person is lying in a busy road. What is the FIRST thing you should do to help?

- Treat the person for shock
- Warn other traffic
- Place them in the recovery position
- Make sure the injured person is kept warm

You have to make a journey in foggy conditions. You should

- follow other vehicles' tail lights closely
- avoid using dipped headlights
- leave plenty of time for your journey
- keep two seconds behind other vehicles

On a clearway you must not stop

- at any time
- when it is busy
- in the rush hour
- during daylight hours

You have stopped at a pelican crossing. A disabled person is crossing slowly in front of you. The lights have now changed to green. You should

- allow the person to cross
- drive in front of the person
- drive behind the person
- sound your horn
- be patient
- edge forward slowly

What will reduce the risk of neck injury resulting from a collision?

- An air-sprung seat
- Anti-lock brakes
- A collapsible steering wheel
- A properly adjusted head restraint

6.7   *Mark **one** answer*

Who is especially in danger of not being seen as you reverse your car?

- ⊙ Motorcyclists
- ⊙ Car drivers
- ⊙ Cyclists
- ⊙ Children

6.8   *Mark **one** answer*

What should the driver of the car approaching the crossing do?

- ⊙ Continue at the same speed
- ⊙ Sound the horn
- ⊙ Drive through quickly
- ⊙ Slow down and get ready to stop

6.9   *Mark **one** answer*

You are driving along this road. The driver on the left is reversing from a driveway. You should

- ⊙ move to the opposite side of the road
- ⊙ drive through as you have priority
- ⊙ sound your horn and be prepared to stop
- ⊙ speed up and drive through quickly

6.10   *Mark **one** answer*

What is the national speed limit on a single carriageway road for cars and motorcycles?

- ⊙ 70 mph
- ⊙ 60 mph
- ⊙ 50 mph
- ⊙ 30 mph

6.11   *Mark **one** answer*

Yellow zigzag lines on the road outside schools mean

- ⊙ sound your horn to alert other road users
- ⊙ stop to allow children to cross
- ⊙ you must not wait or park on these lines
- ⊙ you must not drive over these lines

6.12   *Mark **one** answer*

You have broken down on a motorway. To find the nearest emergency telephone you should always walk

- ⊙ with the traffic flow
- ⊙ facing oncoming traffic
- ⊙ in the direction shown on the marker posts
- ⊙ in the direction of the nearest exit

You are driving through a tunnel and you see this sign. What does it mean?

- ◉ Direction to emergency pedestrian exit
- ◉ Beware of pedestrians, no footpath ahead
- ◉ No access for pedestrians
- ◉ Beware of pedestrians crossing ahead

Front fog lights should be used ONLY when

- ◉ travelling in very light rain
- ◉ visibility is seriously reduced
- ◉ daylight is fading
- ◉ driving after midnight

You are driving in heavy rain. Your steering suddenly becomes very light. You should

- ◉ steer towards the side of the road
- ◉ apply gentle acceleration
- ◉ brake firmly to reduce speed
- ◉ ease off the accelerator

When the traffic lights change to green the white car should

- ◉ wait for the cyclist to pull away
- ◉ move off quickly and turn in front of the cyclist
- ◉ move close up to the cyclist to beat the lights
- ◉ sound the horn to warn the cyclist

If a trailer swerves or snakes when you are towing it you should

- ◉ ease off the accelerator and reduce your speed
- ◉ let go of the steering wheel and let it correct itself
- ◉ brake hard and hold the pedal down
- ◉ increase your speed as quickly as possible

You need to top up your battery. What level should you fill to?

- ◉ The top of the battery
- ◉ Half-way up the battery
- ◉ Just below the cell plates
- ◉ Just above the cell plates

6.19 *Mark one answer*

For what reason may you use the right-hand lane of a motorway?

- ⊙ For keeping out of the way of lorries
- ⊙ For driving at more than 70 mph
- ⊙ For turning right
- ⊙ For overtaking other vehicles

6.20 *Mark one answer*

How can you help to prevent your car radio being stolen?

- ⊙ Park in an unlit area
- ⊙ Hide the radio with a blanket
- ⊙ Park near a busy junction
- ⊙ Install a security-coded radio

6.21 *Mark one answer*

You are having difficulty finding a parking space in a busy town. You can see there is space on the zigzag lines of a zebra crossing. Can you park there?

- ⊙ No, unless you stay with your car
- ⊙ Yes, in order to drop off a passenger
- ⊙ Yes, if you do not block people from crossing
- ⊙ No, not in any circumstances

6.22 *Mark two answers*

You wish to park facing DOWNHILL. Which TWO of the following should you do?

- ⊙ Turn the steering wheel towards the kerb
- ⊙ Park close to the bumper of another car
- ⊙ Park with two wheels on the kerb
- ⊙ Put the handbrake on firmly
- ⊙ Turn the steering wheel away from the kerb

6.23 *Mark one answer*

You intend to turn left at the traffic lights. Just before turning you should

- ⊙ check your right mirror
- ⊙ move close up to the white car
- ⊙ straddle the lanes
- ⊙ check for bicycles on your left

6.24 *Mark two answers*

Your vehicle is insured third party only. This covers

- ⊙ damage to your vehicle
- ⊙ damage to other vehicles
- ⊙ injury to yourself
- ⊙ injury to others
- ⊙ all damage and injury

You are following this lorry. You should keep well back from it to

- ⊙ give you a good view of the road ahead
- ⊙ stop following traffic from rushing through the junction
- ⊙ prevent traffic behind you from overtaking
- ⊙ allow you to hurry through the traffic lights if they change

Which of these is LEAST likely to be affected by crosswinds?

- ⊙ Cyclists
- ⊙ Motorcyclists
- ⊙ High-sided vehicles
- ⊙ Cars

Where should you take particular care to look out for motorcyclists and cyclists?

- ⊙ On dual carriageways
- ⊙ At junctions
- ⊙ At zebra crossings
- ⊙ On one-way streets

What does this sign mean?

- ⊙ Distance to parking place ahead
- ⊙ Distance to public telephone ahead
- ⊙ Distance to public house ahead
- ⊙ Distance to passing place ahead

Which of the following should you NOT do at the scene of an accident?

- ⊙ Warn other traffic by switching on your hazard warning lights
- ⊙ Call the emergency services immediately
- ⊙ Offer someone a cigarette to calm them down
- ⊙ Ask drivers to switch off their engines

What does this sign mean?

- ⊙ Crosswinds
- ⊙ Road noise
- ⊙ Airport
- ⊙ Adverse camber

6.31 *Mark **one** answer*

You are waiting at a T-junction. A vehicle is coming from the right with the left signal flashing. What should you do?

- ⊙ Move out and accelerate hard
- ⊙ Wait until the vehicle starts to turn in
- ⊙ Pull out before the vehicle reaches the junction
- ⊙ Move out slowly

6.32 *Mark **one** answer*

On a motorway this sign means

- ⊙ move over onto the hard shoulder
- ⊙ overtaking on the left only
- ⊙ leave the motorway at the next exit
- ⊙ move to the lane on your left

6.33 *Mark **one** answer*

What should you use your horn for?

- ⊙ To alert others to your presence
- ⊙ To allow you right of way
- ⊙ To greet other road users
- ⊙ To signal your annoyance

6.34 *Mark **one** answer*

This road marking warns

- ⊙ drivers to use the hard shoulder
- ⊙ overtaking drivers there is a bend to the left
- ⊙ overtaking drivers to move back to the left
- ⊙ drivers that it is safe to overtake

6.35 *Mark **two** answers*

You are driving in heavy traffic on a wet road. Spray makes it difficult to be seen. You should use your

- ⊙ full beam headlights
- ⊙ rear fog lights if visibility is less than 100 metres (328 feet)
- ⊙ rear fog lights if visibility is more than 100 metres (328 feet)
- ⊙ dipped headlights
- ⊙ sidelights only

Revision paper seven

7.1　　　Mark **one** answer

What does this sign mean?

- Minimum speed 30 mph
- End of maximum speed
- End of minimum speed
- Maximum speed 30 mph

7.2　　　Mark **one** answer

The cost of your insurance may reduce if you

- are under 25 years old
- do not wear glasses
- pass the driving test first time
- take the Pass Plus scheme

7.3　　　Mark **one** answer

Are passengers allowed to ride in a caravan that is being towed?

- Yes, if they are over fourteen
- No, not at any time
- Only if all the seats in the towing vehicle are full
- Only if a stabiliser is fitted

7.4　　　Mark **one** answer

You are on a busy main road and find that you are travelling in the wrong direction. What should you do?

- Turn into a side road on the right and reverse into the main road
- Make a U-turn in the main road
- Make a 'three-point' turn in the main road
- Turn round in a side road

7.5　　　Mark **one** answer

You are driving past parked cars. You notice a bicycle wheel sticking out between them. What should you do?

- Accelerate past quickly and sound your horn
- Slow down and wave the cyclist across
- Brake sharply and flash your headlights
- Slow down and be prepared to stop for a cyclist

7.6　　　Mark **one** answer

When you are giving mouth to mouth you should only stop when

- you think the casualty is dead
- the casualty can breathe without help
- the casualty has turned blue
- you think the ambulance is coming

7.7   *Mark **one** answer*

'Tailgating' means

- using the rear door of a hatchback car
- reversing into a parking space
- following another vehicle too closely
- driving with rear fog lights on

7.8   *Mark **one** answer*

You want to turn left at this junction. The view of the main road is restricted. What should you do?

- Stay well back and wait to see if something comes
- Build up your speed so that you can emerge quickly
- Stop and apply the handbrake even if the road is clear
- Approach slowly and edge out until you can see more clearly

7.9   *Mark **one** answer*

You are driving a car on a motorway. Unless signs show otherwise you must NOT exceed

- 50 mph
- 60 mph
- 70 mph
- 80 mph

7.10   *Mark **four** answers*

Which of the following may cause loss of concentration on a long journey?

- Loud music
- Arguing with a passenger
- Using a mobile phone
- Putting in a cassette tape
- Stopping regularly to rest
- Pulling up to tune the radio

7.11   *Mark **one** answer*

You are invited to a pub lunch. You know that you will have to drive in the evening. What is your best course of action?

- Avoid mixing your alcoholic drinks
- Not drink any alcohol at all
- Have some milk before drinking alcohol
- Eat a hot meal with your alcoholic drinks

7.12   *Mark **one** answer*

You are driving a vehicle fitted with anti-lock brakes. You need to stop in an emergency. You should apply the footbrake

- slowly and gently
- slowly but firmly
- rapidly and gently
- rapidly and firmly

7.13 *Mark one answer*

When approaching a right-hand bend you should keep well to the left. Why is this?

- ⊙ To improve your view of the road
- ⊙ To overcome the effect of the road's slope
- ⊙ To let faster traffic from behind overtake
- ⊙ To be positioned safely if you skid

7.14 *Mark two answers*

You are travelling behind a bus that pulls up at a bus stop. What should you do?

- ⊙ Accelerate past the bus sounding your horn
- ⊙ Watch carefully for pedestrians
- ⊙ Be ready to give way to the bus
- ⊙ Pull in closely behind the bus

7.15 *Mark one answer*

How will a police officer in a patrol vehicle normally get you to stop?

- ⊙ Flash the headlights, indicate left and point to the left
- ⊙ Wait until you stop, then approach you
- ⊙ Use the siren, overtake, cut in front and stop
- ⊙ Pull alongside you, use the siren and wave you to stop

7.16 *Mark one answer*

You are approaching this cyclist. You should

- ⊙ overtake before the cyclist gets to the junction
- ⊙ flash your headlights at the cyclist
- ⊙ slow down and allow the cyclist to turn
- ⊙ overtake the cyclist on the left-hand side

7.17 *Mark one answer*

You are on a three-lane motorway towing a trailer. You may use the right-hand lane when

- ⊙ there are lane closures
- ⊙ there is slow moving traffic
- ⊙ you can maintain a high speed
- ⊙ large vehicles are in the left and centre lanes

7.18 *Mark one answer*

What does this motorway sign mean?

- ⊙ Change to the lane on your left
- ⊙ Leave the motorway at the next exit
- ⊙ Change to the opposite carriageway
- ⊙ Pull up on the hard shoulder

7.19   *Mark **one** answer*

What does this sign mean?

- ○ Quayside or river bank
- ○ Steep hill downwards
- ○ Uneven road surface
- ○ Road liable to flooding

7.20   *Mark **one** answer*

What does this signal from a police officer, mean to oncoming traffic?

- ○ Go ahead
- ○ Stop
- ○ Turn left
- ○ Turn right

7.21   *Mark **one** answer*

You are going through a congested tunnel and have to stop. What should you do?

- ○ Pull up very close to the vehicle in front to save space
- ○ Ignore any message signs as they are never up to date
- ○ Keep a safe distance from the vehicle in front
- ○ Make a U-turn and find another route

7.22   *Mark **three** answers*

You are going along a street with parked vehicles on the left-hand side. For which THREE reasons should you keep your speed down?

- ○ So that oncoming traffic can see you more clearly
- ○ You may set off car alarms
- ○ Vehicles may be pulling out
- ○ Drivers' doors may open
- ○ Children may run out from between the vehicles

7.23   *Mark **one** answer*

You have just passed your test. How can you decrease your risk of accidents on the motorway?

- ○ By keeping up with the car in front
- ○ By never going over 40 mph
- ○ By staying only in the left-hand lane
- ○ By taking further training

7.24   *Mark **one** answer*

What does this sign mean?

- ○ New speed limit 20 mph
- ○ No vehicles over 30 tonnes
- ○ Minimum speed limit 30 mph
- ○ End of 20 mph zone

In which THREE of these situations may you overtake another vehicle on the left?

- ⊙ When you are in a one-way street
- ⊙ When approaching a motorway slip road where you will be turning off
- ⊙ When the vehicle in front is signalling to turn right
- ⊙ When a slower vehicle is travelling in the right-hand lane of a dual carriageway
- ⊙ In slow-moving traffic queues when traffic in the right-hand lane is moving more slowly

You are following a large lorry on a wet road. Spray makes it difficult to see. You should

- ⊙ drop back until you can see better
- ⊙ put your headlights on full beam
- ⊙ keep close to the lorry, away from the spray
- ⊙ speed up and overtake quickly

Unbalanced wheels on a car may cause

- ⊙ the steering to pull to one side
- ⊙ the steering to vibrate
- ⊙ the brakes to fail
- ⊙ the tyres to deflate

Which THREE of the following will affect your stopping distance?

- ⊙ How fast you are going
- ⊙ The tyres on your vehicle
- ⊙ The time of day
- ⊙ The weather
- ⊙ The street lighting

You are driving past a line of parked cars. You notice a ball bouncing out into the road ahead. What should you do?

- ⊙ Continue driving at the same speed and sound your horn
- ⊙ Continue driving at the same speed and flash your headlights
- ⊙ Slow down and be prepared to stop for children
- ⊙ Stop and wave the children across to fetch their ball

As a driver, you can help reduce pollution levels in town centres by

- ⊙ driving more quickly
- ⊙ over-revving in a low gear
- ⊙ walking or cycling
- ⊙ driving short journeys

7.31   *Mark **one** answer*

The legal minimum depth of tread for car tyres over three quarters of the breadth is

- ⊙ 1 mm
- ⊙ 1.6 mm
- ⊙ 2.5 mm
- ⊙ 4 mm

7.32   *Mark **one** answer*

Which sign means you have priority over oncoming vehicles?

7.33   *Mark **one** answer*

You are approaching a red light at a puffin crossing. Pedestrians are on the crossing. The red light will stay on until

- ⊙ you start to edge forward on to the crossing
- ⊙ the pedestrians have reached a safe position
- ⊙ the pedestrians are clear of the front of your vehicle
- ⊙ a driver from the opposite direction reaches the crossing

7.34   *Mark **one** answer*

Motorcyclists should wear bright clothing mainly because

- ⊙ they must do so by law
- ⊙ it helps keep them cool in summer
- ⊙ the colours are popular
- ⊙ drivers often do not see them

7.35   *Mark **one** answer*

Which of these, if allowed to get low, could cause an accident?

- ⊙ Anti-freeze level
- ⊙ Brake fluid level
- ⊙ Battery water level
- ⊙ Radiator coolant level

1.1 keep both hands on the wheel

1.2 dazzle other drivers

1.3 60 mph

1.4 carry on with great care

1.5 keep them in the vehicle

1.6 Apply firm pressure to the wound

1.7 engage the steering lock

1.8 On the exhaust system

1.9 Injury to another person

Damage to someone's property

Damage to other vehicles

1.10 Release the footbrake fully

1.11 Two-way traffic straight ahead

1.12

1.13 No waiting zone ends

1.14

1.15 steering control when braking

1.16 It is to separate traffic flowing in opposite directions

1.17 In a well-lit area

1.18 Cycles

1.19 On a school bus

1.20 Reduce speed until you are clear of the area

1.21 reduce speed in good time

choose an appropriate lane early

keep the correct separation distance

1.22 check for traffic overtaking on your right

1.23 50 mph

1.24 Traffic in both directions can use the middle lane to overtake

1.25 steering

tyres

1.26 To get the best view of the road ahead

1.27 Switch on your hazard warning lights

1.28 slow down or stop

1.29 To allow vehicles to enter and emerge

1.30 exempt for medical reasons

1.31 Keep well back

1.32 buses

1.33 A baby carrier

1.34 look for motorcyclists filtering through the traffic

1.35 give way to pedestrians who are crossing

2.1 You will have to pay the first £100 of any claim

2.2 Lorries are longer than cars

2.3 End of dual carriageway

2.4 No through road on the left

2.5 Go home by public transport

2.6 be easily seen by others

2.7 Learner car drivers

Farm tractors

Learner motorcyclists

Cyclists

2.8 Slow down

2.9 The bus may move out into the road

2.10 go slowly while gently applying the brakes

2.11 Green

2.12 At all times when driving

2.13 In a garage

2.14 slow down and prepare to stop

2.15 Switch them off as long as visibility remains good

2.16 seek medical assistance

2.17 stay well back and give it room

2.18 stop at the next service area and rest

leave the motorway at the next exit and rest

2.19 Cyclists

Motorcyclists

Pedestrians

2.20 Any direction

2.21 Danger ahead

2.22 windows

lights

mirrors

number plates

2.23 breathing

2.24 wait for them to cross

2.25 The right-hand lane is closed

2.26 you must stop and wait behind the stop line

2.27 lock them out of sight

2.28 Windscreen pillars

2.29 your vehicle is broken down on the hard shoulder

2.30 Switch on your own hazard warning lights

Make sure that someone telephones for an ambulance

Get people who are not injured clear of the scene

2.31 braking system

suspension

2.32 30%

2.33 When in an accident were damage or injury is caused

At a red traffic light

When signalled to do so by a police officer

2.34 Carrying unnecessary weight

Under-inflated tyres

A fitted, empty roof rack

2.35 steering

handling

Answers **Paper three**

3.1 Keep injured people warm and comfortable

Keep injured people calm by talking to them reassuringly

Make sure that injured people are not left alone

3.2 Park in a well-lit area

3.3 70 mph

3.4 You, the driver

3.5

3.6 dipped headlights

3.7 On a free-flowing motorway or dual carriageway

3.8 'give way' sign

3.9 a clear view of the crossing area

3.10 skid

3.11 The cyclist crossing the road

3.12 Pedestrian crossing ahead

3.13 Brake lights are less clear

Following drivers can be dazzled

3.14 A valid driving licence with signature

A valid tax disc displayed on your vehicle

Proper insurance cover

3.15 A vehicle towing a trailer

3.16 Keep going and clear the crossing

3.17 during its period of operation

3.18 Doctor's car

3.19 This could result in more serious injury

3.20 Be prepared to stop for any traffic.

3.21 Lock valuables out of sight

3.22 Making sure that you get plenty of fresh air

Making regular stops for refreshments

3.23 give way to pedestrians already on the crossing

3.24 loose

wet

3.25	Watch out for pedestrians walking in the road
3.26	slowly, leaving plenty of room
3.27	To avoid misleading other road users
3.28	Before a long journey
3.29	Continuous high speeds may increase the risk of your vehicle breaking down
3.30	Pull over at a safe place to rest
3.31	not exceed 60 mph
	use only the left and centre lanes
3.32	stay behind
3.33	deaf
3.34	Do not overtake, stay well back and be prepared to stop.
3.35	Slow down and be prepared to wait

Answers **Paper four**

4.1	on a steep gradient
4.2	Cycle route ahead
4.3	lock it and remove the key
4.4	On a motorway slip road
4.5	calm down before you start to drive
4.6	reduce harmful exhaust emissions
4.7	When tyres are cold
4.8	go to the next emergency telephone and inform the police
4.9	No parking at any time
4.10	The cyclist is slower and more vulnerable
4.11	Taking a Pass Plus course
4.12	stop in a safe place
4.13	Visibility along the major road is restricted
4.14	on your own
	on the motorway
4.15	At slip road entrances and exits
4.16	Slow down and give way
4.17	remove the key and lock it

4.18	
4.19	Dipped headlights
4.20	When driving fast for a long distance
	When carrying a heavy load
4.21	Stop before the barrier
4.22	leave the motorway at the next exit
4.23	53 metres (175 feet)
4.24	press the brake pedal promptly and firmly until you have stopped
4.25	With-flow pedal cycle lane
4.26	with parking lights on
4.27	Reduce your speed and increase the gap
4.28	stop and switch off your engine
4.29	Be prepared to stop behind
4.30	Not at any time
4.31	Stop at the scene of the accident
4.32	good
4.33	continue in that lane
4.34	Left lane
4.35	at least 45 metres (147 feet) behind your vehicle

Answers **Paper five**

5.1	They are countdown markers to the next exit
5.2	have held a full licence for at least 3 years
	be at least 21 years old
5.3	No one has priority
5.4	To make them more visible in thick fog
5.5	No stopping
5.6	indicate left before leaving the roundabout
5.7	Roundabout
5.8	be medically fit to drive
	not drive after taking certain medicines
5.9	on the motorway

5.10   No motorcycles

5.11

5.12   Look out for variable message signs

5.13   To prevent the junction becoming blocked

5.14   reversing

5.15   Your vehicle will pick up speed

5.16   Pedestrians

5.17   travel at a reduced speed

5.18   Stop and give way

5.19   check out the problem quickly and safely

5.20   Be prepared to stop

5.21   Give an arm signal as well as using
            your indicator

5.22   allow extra room in case they swerve
            to avoid potholes

5.23   find a safe place to stop

5.24   Slow down very gradually

5.25   Drive slowly past
            Give plenty of room

5.26   By reducing your speed
            By gentle acceleration
            By servicing your vehicle properly

5.27   use public transport more often
            share a car when possible
            walk or cycle on short journeys

5.28   Etching the car number on the windows

5.29   in operation 24 hours a day

5.30   Pedestrians stepping out between cars
            Doors opening on parked cars
            Cars leaving parking spaces

5.31   Remove all valuables

5.32   keep a safe gap

5.33   dipped headlights

5.34

5.35   Because they cannot steer to avoid you

6.1   not overtake if you are in doubt

6.2   Warn other traffic

6.3   leave plenty of time for your journey

6.4   at any time

6.5   allow the person to cross
           be patient

6.6   A properly adjusted head restraint

6.7   Children

6.8   Slow down and get ready to stop

6.9   sound your horn and be prepared to stop

6.10   60 mph

6.11   you must not wait or park on these lines

6.12   in the direction shown on the marker posts

6.13   Direction to emergency pedestrian exit

6.14   visibility is seriously reduced

6.15   ease off the accelerator

6.16   wait for the cyclist to pull away

6.17   ease off the accelerator and reduce
           your speed

6.18   Just above the cell plates

6.19   For overtaking other vehicles

6.20   Install a security-coded radio

6.21   No, not in any circumstances

6.22   Turn the steering wheel towards the kerb
           Put the handbrake on firmly

6.23   check for bicycles on your left

6.24   damage to other vehicles
           injury to others

6.25   give you a good view of the road ahead

6.26   Cars

6.27   At junctions

6.28   Distance to parking place ahead

6.29   Offer someone a cigarette to calm
           them down

6.30   Crosswinds

6.31   Wait until the vehicle starts to turn in

6.32 move to the lane on your left

6.33 To alert others to your presence

6.34 overtaking drivers to move back to the left

6.35 rear fog lights if visibility is less than 100 metres (328 feet)

dipped headlights

Answers **Paper seven**

7.1 End of minimum speed

7.2 take the Pass Plus scheme

7.3 No, not at any time

7.4 Turn round in a side road

7.5 Slow down and be prepared to stop for a cyclist

7.6 the casualty can breathe without help

7.7 following another vehicle too closely

7.8 Approach slowly and edge out until you can see more clearly

7.9 70 mph

7.10 Loud music

Arguing with a passenger

Using a mobile phone

Putting in a cassette tape

7.11 Not drink any alcohol at all

7.12 rapidly and firmly

7.13 To improve your view of the road

7.14 Watch carefully for pedestrians

Be ready to give way to the bus

7.15 Flash the headlights, indicate left and point to the left

7.16 slow down and allow the cyclist to turn

7.17 there are lane closures

7.18 Change to the lane on your left

7.19 Quayside or river bank

7.20 Stop

7.21 Keep a safe distance from the vehicle in front

7.22 Vehicles may be pulling out

Drivers' doors may open

Children may run out from between the vehicles

7.23 By taking further training

7.24 End of 20 mph zone

7.25 When you are in a one-way street

When the vehicle in front is signalling to turn right

In slow-moving traffic queues when traffic in the right-hand lane is moving more slowly

7.26 drop back until you can see better

7.27 the steering to vibrate

7.28 How fast you are going

The tyres on your vehicle

The weather

7.29 Slow down and be prepared to stop for children

7.30 walking or cycling

7.31 1.6 mm

7.32

7.33 the pedestrians have reached a safe position

7.34 drivers often do not see them

7.35 Brake fluid level

the *official* guide to
HAZARD
PERCEPTION
DVD

The only official guide to the hazard perception part of the tests. Hazard perception is a key part of today's driving tests and this interactive DVD will help boost your driving skills and prepare you for the tests and beyond.

- Plays on DVD players (with a TV and DVD remote), DVD enabled computers and most games consoles. Check your console manual for compatibility
- Clear guidance on how to recognise and respond to hazards on the road
- Packed with useful tips, quizzes and expert advice to help you get on the road safely
- Includes the official DSA hazard perception video clips with feedback on your performance
- Watch out for the sample multiple choice theory test questions at the end of each section to test your knowledge
- Hard of hearing sub-titles option
- English voice-over option
- Information about what happens at the theory test centre

0 11 552494 0 £15.99 inc VAT

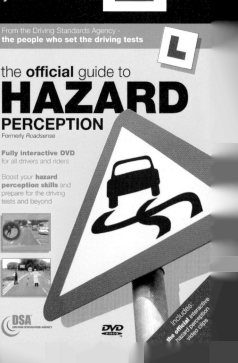

From the Driving Standards Agency -
the people who set the driving tests

the **official** guide to
HAZARD
PERCEPTION
Formerly *Roadsense*

Fully interactive DVD
for all drivers and riders

Boost your **hazard
perception skills** and
prepare for the driving
tests and beyond

DSA
DRIVING STANDARDS AGENCY

DVD
VIDEO

includes:
the official interactive
hazard perception
video clips

5 Easy Ways to Order The DSA Range

Online
Visit www.tso.co.uk/dsa

By Telephone
Please call 0870 243 0123

By Fax
Please fax orders to 0870 243 0129

By Post
Please send orders to
Marketing, TSO,
Freepost ANG 4748,
Norwich NR3 1YX
(No stamp required)

TSO Shops
Visit your local TSO Shop

Please quote ref **CQD**